THIS
JOURNAL
DONATES
ONE ITEM